BOOK 1

MASTER YOUR SPELLING

**Geoff Davies
Sue Dillon
and
Terry Dillon**

STANLEY
THORNES

Text © Geoff Davies, Sue Dillon and Terry Dillon 1993
Artwork © Stanley Thornes

First edition published in 1983 by
Basil Blackwell Ltd

Second edition published in 1993 by
Simon & Schuster Education

Reprinted in 1994

Reprinted in 1995 by
Stanley Thornes Publishers Ltd
Ellenborough House
Wellington Street
Cheltenham GL50 1YW

  98 99 00 / 10 9 8 7 6 5 4

A catalogue record of this book is available from the British
Library.

ISBN 0 7487 2488 5

Design and typesetting by Can Do Design
Illustrated by Roger Backwell
Printed in the United Kingdom by Redwood Books, Trowbridge

Contents

How to Master your Spelling

To learn the words in this book:

do the activities.

Then, for each word you don't already know well:

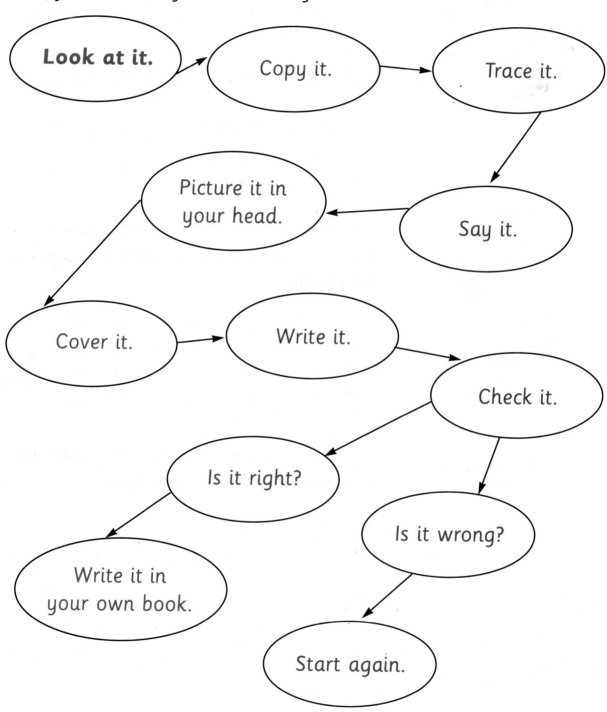

The alphabet

There are 26 letters in the alphabet. Say them to yourself.

a	b	c	d	e	f	g	h	i	j	k	l	m
1	2	3	4	5	6	7	8	9	10	11	12	13
n	o	p	q	r	s	t	u	v	w	x	y	z
14	15	16	17	18	19	20	21	22	23	24	25	26

1 Each of the numbers on the right stands for a letter of the alphabet.

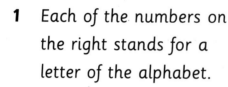

Find out which letters the numbers below stand for. Write down the words they make in your book.

a	3	1	20		**e**	19	21	14
b	20	5	14		**f**	8	1	20
c	3	1	18		**g**	5	7	7
d	2	5	4		**h**	2	15	24

2 Choose three of the words you have made and draw a picture to go with each one.

3 Ranjit has written out his alphabet, but has missed out some letters. Help him to put them in. Write the alphabet in your book and put in the missing letters.

a b c   e g h i k n o p q s t u w x y

4 Ranjit has now mixed up the alphabet. Put the letters back into the correct order.

ghi

jkl

vwx

pqr

stu

mno

yz

abc

def

Capital letters

Here is the alphabet in capital letters.

A	B	C	D	E	F	G	H	I	J	K	L	M
1	2	3	4	5	6	7	8	9	10	11	12	13

N	O	P	Q	R	S	T	U	V	W	X	Y	Z
14	15	16	17	18	19	20	21	22	23	24	25	26

1 What is the first letter of the alphabet?

2 What is the last letter of the alphabet?

3 Write the words below in your book and underline the capital letters.

a	Mum	**h**	London
b	Sam	**i**	Dad
c	Joanne	**j**	Superman
d	Andrew	**k**	Monday
e	Katie	**l**	Christmas
f	Daniel	**m**	Nicola
g	Rebecca	**n**	Friday

4 Write down your name and the names of four of your friends. Remember the capital letters.

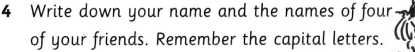

Vowels

a   e   i   o   u

a b c d **e** f g h **i** j k l m
n **o** p q r s t **u** v w x y z

1 The letters above in **bold** have a special name. They are called **vowels**. Write down in your book all the words in the word-fish that start with a vowel.

into   up   led

his   big   old   box

egg   ear   ivy   dog

fox   pin   open   my

and   acorn   up   art

leg   met

All about me

My name is Sarah.

Dad   **brother**   **family**   **Mum**   **years**   **sister**

1   Use the words under the pictures to complete the sentences below.

   a I am seven y _ _ _ _ old.

   b This is my f _ _ _ _ _ .

   c My D _ _ likes gardening.

   d My M _ _ is mending the car.

   e Joe is my little b _ _ _ _ _ _ .

   f Emma is my big s _ _ _ _ _ .

2   Copy the sentences below into your book. Write in the words that are missing from the sentences. They are about you and nobody else.

   a My name is _____.

   b I am _____ years old .

   c My best friend is called _____.

   d My address is _____.

   e My favourite food is _____.

   f I go to _____ School.

Short vowel a

1 Complete the words under the pictures.
Write them in your book.

v _ n

t _ p

r _ t

h _ t

s _ d

b _ t

b _ g

c _ t

2 Fill in the blanks in the sentences below.
Write them in your book.

a Grandma has a new h _ t.
b A clown is a funny m _ n.
c A b _ t flies at night.
d Turn off the t _ p, please.
e Ben's book is in his school b _ g.
f Uncle Bill gave his c _ t a saucer of milk.

Short vowel e

1 Complete the words below. Write them in your book and draw a picture for each word.

l _ g   t _ n
r _ d   p _ n
w _ t   _ gg
w _ b

2 Complete the sentences below by filling in the missing letters. Write them in your book.

a Andrew got very w _ t in the rain.
b Hannah writes with a p _ n.
c The h _ _ laid an egg.
d Mina goes to b _ d at 8 o'clock.
e A spider spins a fine w _ b.
f Steven fell and cut his l _ g.
g Five and five makes t _ n.
h Yasar kicked the ball into the n _ t.

Short vowel i

1 Fill in the missing **i** in the words under the flags. Write the words in your book.

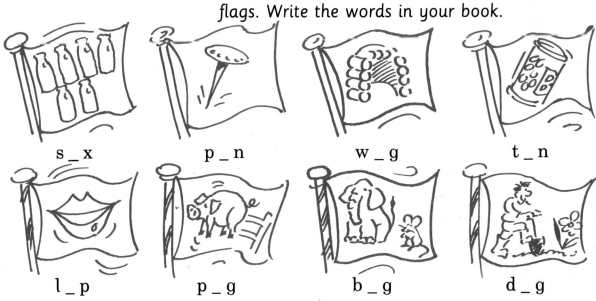

s _ x   p _ n   w _ g   t _ n

l _ p   p _ g   b _ g   d _ g

2 Use the words in the box to complete the sentences below.

bin	bit	fin	hit
lid	lip	sit	tip

a Tom h _ _ Nayan on the nose.

b The b _ _ was full of rubbish.

c He has a cut on the t _ _ of his finger.

d I only had a little b _ _ of cake for tea.

e Ahmed put the l _ _ on the jar.

f Our cat likes to s _ _ in front of the fire.

g Sally fell and cut her l _ _ .

h The shark has a big f _ _ .

Short vowel o

1 Write down the words below in your book.
Fill in the missing letters.

b _ x   j _ b   d _ g   p _ t

c _ t   h _ t   p _ p   f _ g

2 Choose a word from the box below to complete each of
the sentences. Write them in your book.

box	**cot**	**dog**	**fog**
hot	**job**	**pot**	**top**

a I have a j _ _ for you to do.
b Dad gave Mum a b _ _ of chocolates.
c My baby sister sleeps in a c _ _ _ .
d Nicola climbed to the t _ _ of the tree.
e Rudolph helped Santa find his way in the f _ _ .
f Put two tea bags in the p _ _ _ .
g Tom has a pet d _ _ .
h That iron is h _ _ _ .

Short vowel u

1 Fill in the missing letters below.

Write the words you make in your book.

b _ s	m _ d	n _ t	r _ n
g _ n	p _ t	h _ t	c _ t

2 Use the words in the box to help you fill in the missing letters in the sentences below. Write the sentences in your book.

bun	cup	dug	fun	hum
	mug	Mum	sun	

a Dad d _ g a big hole in the garden.

b We made a wholemeal b _ n for tea.

c It is too hot in the s _ _ .

d Tom's M _ m put him to bed.

e I can h _ m the tune.

f Can I have a c _ p of tea, please?

g Amy dropped her m _ g of coffee.

h We had lots of f _ n at the fair.

The seasons

1 Match each picture to a season. Draw the pictures in your book and write the correct season underneath.

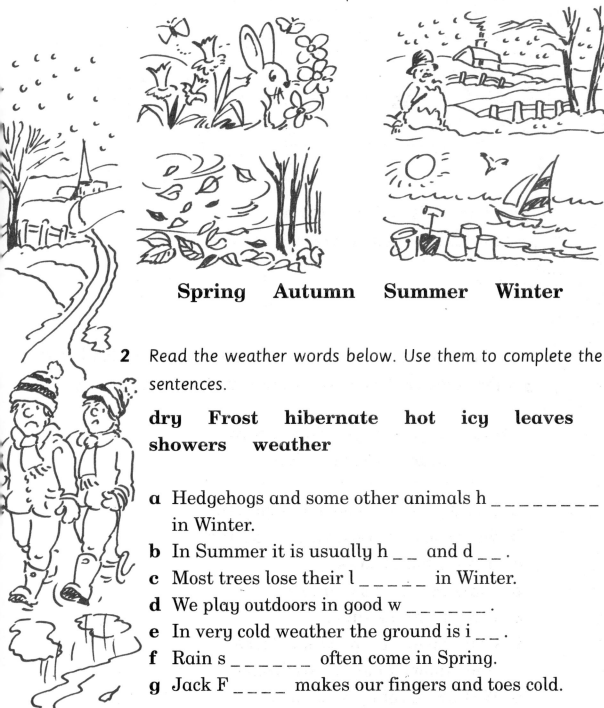

Spring   Autumn   Summer   Winter

2 Read the weather words below. Use them to complete the sentences.

**dry   Frost   hibernate   hot   icy   leaves
showers   weather**

a Hedgehogs and some other animals h _ _ _ _ _ _ _ _
in Winter.

b In Summer it is usually h _ _ and d _ _ .

c Most trees lose their l _ _ _ _ _ in Winter.

d We play outdoors in good w _ _ _ _ _ _ .

e In very cold weather the ground is i _ _ .

f Rain s _ _ _ _ _ _ often come in Spring.

g Jack F _ _ _ _ makes our fingers and toes cold.

Testing time

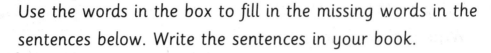

1 Use the words in the box to fill in the missing words in the sentences below. Write the sentences in your book.

brother   **dig**   **end**   **fit**   **friend**   **fun**   **had**   **hops**   **jam**   **pet**   **Spring**   **Summer**   **telephone**   **top**   **up**   **weather**

a Rosie's shoes don't f _ _ her any more.

b Divia has two p _ _ rabbits.

c A frog _ _ p _ along.

d Tom's party was a lot of f _ _ .

e Sarah loves bread and strawberry j _ _ .

f Start work at the t _ _ of the page.

g Craig helped to d _ _ the garden.

h Have you h _ _ your tea yet?

i That's the e _ _ of the story.

j Get _ _ quickly, or you'll be late.

k Sophie is Joanne's best f _ _ _ _ _ .

l We expect cold w _ _ _ _ _ r in Winter.

m In S _ _ _ _ g new leaves grow on the trees.

n My t _ _ _ _ _ _ _ e number is 865790.

o My b _ _ _ _ _ r Nicholas is older than I am.

p S _ _ _ _ r is a time to go on picnics.

y

1 Put **y** on the end of each of the words under the pictures.
Write the words in your book.

a lorr

b lad

c marr

d funn

e happ

2 Use the shape clues to help you to complete the
sentences below.

☐	⬭	◻	△	◯
buy	**fry**	**sty**	**try**	**Why**

a Please △ to finish your work quickly.

b Dad likes to ⬭ bacon for breakfast.

c A pig lives in a ◻ .

d Elizabeth loves to ☐ sweets.

e ◯ are you crying?

ay

1 Add **ay** to complete the words below.
Write them in your book.

  a r _ _
  b aw _ _
  c d _ _
  d s _ _
  e h _ _
  f w _ _
  g tr _ _
  h cl _ _

2 Use the words you have made to complete the sentences below.

  a What did you s _ _?
  b Victoria loves to play football every d _ _ .
  c Adrian ran a _ _ _ from the big dog.
  d Horses love to eat h _ _ .
  e The r _ _ of sunlight shone through the window.
  f Which w _ _ shall we go?
  g Gran carried the mugs on a t _ _ _ .
  h Ranjit made a vase out of cl _ _ .

a and e

1 Look at the pictures above and write the words
for them in your book. All the words start with the letter in **bold**.

a ak**c**e   **b** **k**ale   **c** es**c**a   **d** e**a**k**r**   **e** na**k**se

2 Choose the correct word from above the cake to complete
the sentences below.

made   **mane**   **name**   **pale**   **take**   **wake**

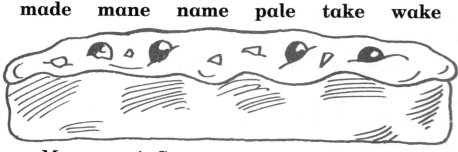

a My n _ _ _ is Susan.
b John looked p _ _ _ and ill.
c Sarah was so tired Mum could not w _ _ _ her.
d James m _ _ _ his Grandad a birthday card.
e Georgina brushed the horse's m _ _ _ _ .
f I t _ _ _ a packed lunch to school every day.

i and e

1 The magician has added a magic **e** which makes the letter say its name.

hid hide   spin spine
rid ride   rip ripe

Choose the correct words from the pot to complete the sentences below. Write them in your book.

a My Dad likes to drink w _ _ _ .

b Emma polished her shoes to make them s _ _ _ _ .

c Tom did not l _ _ _ his supper.

d The weather was f _ _ _ today.

e A p _ _ _ tree does not lose its leaves in the Winter.

f That coat is m _ _ _ not yours.

mine
like
wine
shine
pine
fine

2 Use the words in the toy box to complete the sentences below. Write them in your book.

dive	drive	hide	ride	slide	time

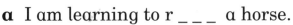

a I am learning to r _ _ _ a horse.

b Tom and Ben played h _ _ _ and seek.

c Sally has a watch but cannot tell the t _ _ _ .

d My big sister is learning to dr _ _ _ .

e All the children had to d _ _ _ in the pool.

f We like to s _ _ _ _ on the ice.

o and e

1 Draw these pictures in your book. Choose the correct word from the list below to go with each picture.

roll	bowl	hide	rose	near	comb
ripe	bone	hold	role	nose	case
rope	bun	hole	ripe	nice	mole

2 The words below in **bold** are jumbled up. Write out the sentences in your book and fill in the words correctly.

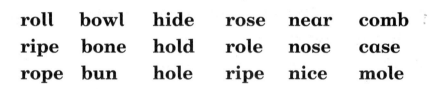

bone   hose   joke   rode   smoke   woke

a The dog chewed his **oebn**.
b The baby screamed and **kweo** Dad.
c Kate **erdo** off fast on her bike.
d David laughed at the funny **koej**.
e Gran used the **sheo** to water the garden.
f A puff of **mkose** rose from the chimney.

21

u and e

1 Use the words in the box to complete the sentences below.

cube	**flute**	**huge**	**June**	**tube**	**tune**

a The musician loves to play his f _ _ _ _ .

b The month after J _ _ _ is July.

c Dad bought Mum a h _ _ _ card on her birthday.

d Matthew made a c _ _ _ in the maths lesson.

e Can you play this t _ _ _ ?

f Jane rolled the paper into a long t _ _ _ .

2 Find the words to match the meanings.

a an important person   **flute**

b a musical instrument   **rude**

c not polite or pleasant   **fuse**

d a part of an electric plug   **duke**

ll

1 Use the words in the box to complete the sentences below.
Write them in your book.

bell	fill	hill	ill	sell	well

a The b _ _ _ rings at the end of playtime.
b Daniel rode his bike down the h _ _ _ _ .
c Kate was i _ _ and could not come to school.
d Mum had to s _ _ _ her old car and buy another one.
e Richard did not feel very w _ _ _ .
f Please f _ _ _ the jug with water.

2 Use the words in the box to complete the
sentences below. Write them in your book.

bill	fell	pill	shell	spill	tell

a A heron has a very long b _ _ _ .
b Rebecca found a sh _ _ _ on the beach.
c Tim f _ _ _ over and cut his knee.
d Please t _ _ _ me a story.
e Thomas took a p _ _ _ for his headache.
f Be careful not to sp _ _ _ your drink.

Special days

1 Match the pictures to the word clues. Draw the pictures in your book. Write the words underneath.

a Christmas   **c** presents   **e** reindeer
b Guy Fawkes'   **d** Passover

2 Use the words to fill in the blanks below and complete the sentences.

a Jews celebrate the P _ _ _ o _ _ _ for eight days.
b C _ _ _ _ _ _ _ _ Day is 25 December.
c G _ _ F _ _ _ _ _ night is on 5 November.
d Rudolf is Santa's best r _ _ _ _ _ _ _ .
e At Christmas time we have p _ _ _ _ _ _ _ .

ee

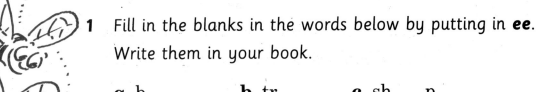

1 Fill in the blanks in the words below by putting in **ee**.
Write them in your book.

a b _ _   **b** tr _ _   **c** sh _ _ p

d w _ _ d   **e** h _ _ l   **f** sl _ _ p

2 Use the words in the box to complete the sentences below.

been	**deep**	**feel**	**heel**	**jeep**	**meet**
needs	**peel**	**see**	**seed**	**seen**	**week**

a Sophie is thirsty and she n _ _ _ _ a drink.

b Christopher has to m _ _ _ his Mum after school.

c That pool is very d _ _ _ _ .

d There are seven days in a w _ _ _ _ .

e Darren grew this plant from a s _ _ _ .

f Your h _ _ _ is part of your foot.

g The skin of an orange is called the p _ _ _ _ .

h Have you s _ _ _ my book?

i A blind person cannot s _ _ .

j The soldier drove an army j _ _ _ _ .

k Where have you b _ _ _ ?

l I f _ _ _ sick.

oo

1 Add **oo** to each of the words below.
Write them in your book.

a m _ _ n   **b** r _ _ f   **c** h _ _ p

d b _ _ t   **e** t _ _ th   **f** h _ _k

2 Use the words in the box to complete the sentences below.
Write them in your book.

broom	**pool**	**room**	**school**	**soon**

a Tom swept the floor with the b _ _ _ _ .

b There was not enough r _ _ _ to fit everyone
in the car.

c Rachel was late for s _ _ _ _ _ this morning.

d It will s _ _ _ be time to go to bed.

e The children all jumped into the p _ _ _ .

3 Look at the clues in the box. Copy the grid into your
book and fill it in.

book	**cook**	**foot**	**hook**	**wood**

a | b | **oo** | k | something you read

b | c | **oo** | k | bottom part of your leg

c | f | **oo** | t | you hang your coat on this

d | | **oo** | | a tree is made of this

e | | **oo** | | we do this to food

Colours

1 Match the colours to the pictures above.
Write them in your book.

a white   **b** yellow   **c** red
d black   **e** green

2 Match these balloons to make colours.
Write the colours in your book.

a wh _ _ _   een

b bla _ _   ow

c gr _ _ _   ue

d yell _ _   ck

e bl _ _   ite

3 Match the beginnings to the correct endings
to find some more colours.

a pur _ _ _   nk
b vio _ _ _   ey
c pi _ _   ple
d gr _ _   let

27

Word stop

1 Use the words in the box to complete the sentences below. Write them in your book.

blue	busy	cone	green	holiday
kill	make	party	play	pool
prize	rude	size	sleep	

a On Saturday I am going to Emma's birthday p _ _ _ _ .

b Dad put the baby to s _ _ _ _ in the cot.

c Ben dived into the swimming p _ _ _ .

d We could not go out to p _ _ _ because it was too wet.

e Poor Tom dropped his ice-cream c _ _ _ in the mud.

f The shoes did not fit because they were the wrong s _ _ _ .

g A policeman wears a b _ _ _ uniform with silver buttons.

h The teacher is b _ _ _ marking books.

i We are going on h _ _ _ _ _ _ to the seaside.

j I help my Mum to m _ _ _ cakes.

k My Dad won first p _ _ _ _ in the Fathers' race.

l It is very cruel to k _ _ _ spiders.

m Dad was cross because Lucy had been so r _ _ _ _ .

n The tiny plant had bright g _ _ _ _ _ leaves.

er

1 Use the words in the box to complete the sentences below.

another   butter   farmer   father flower   letter   sister   thunder

a The f _ _ _ _ _ has to feed the animals early in the morning.

b Peter's f _ _ _ _ _ is a very tall man.

c Alice hated the bread and b _ _ _ _ _ pudding.

d We put the l _ _ _ _ _ into the postbox.

e My s _ _ _ _ _ is two years older than I am.

f Everyone was frightened of the th _ _ _ _ _ and lightning.

g I would like a _ _ _ _ _ _ drink, please.

h The f _ _ _ _ _ had red and yellow petals.

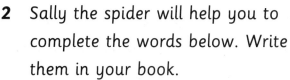

2 Sally the spider will help you to complete the words below. Write them in your book.

a driv
b writ
c clev
d spid

e teach
f lett
g broth

er

or

1 Use the words in the box to complete the sentences below.

| born   doctor   forgot |
| horses   sort |

a The d _ _ _ _ _ said I was not to go to school.

b I was b _ _ _ in December.

c Rachel helped her Dad to s _ _ _ the clothes.

d Nayan f _ _ _ _ _ his packed lunch.

e I love to feed the h _ _ _ _ _ .

2 Add **or** to complete the words below. Write them in your book.

a c _ _ n

b rep _ _ t

c s _ _ e

d sh _ _ ts

e w _ _ n

f t _ _ n

ck nk sk

1 Use the words in the box to complete the sentences below.

ask	mask	neck	sank
sick	tank	task	wink

a Simon was s _ _ _ after eating too much.

b The paper boat s _ _ _ in the water.

c Please a _ _ if you do not understand.

d The robber was wearing a m _ _ _ .

e A giraffe has a very long n _ _ _ .

f The soldier drove the t _ _ _ .

g Ben can w _ _ _ .

h It was a very hard t _ _ _ .

2 Put the words below into the correct goals. Write them in your book.

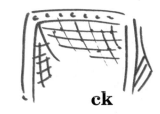

nk   **sk**   **ck**

a dock	**b** rank	**c** task	**d** pick	**e** bank
f sick	**g** peck	**h** sink	**i** pink	**j** deck
k tick	**l** kick	**m** think	**n** tank	**o** ask
p mask	**q** lock	**r** ski	**s** skate	**t** skill

ch sh

1 Use the words in the box to complete the sentences below.

chat	chest	chicks	chimney
chin	chips	chop	church

a I love fish and c _ _ _ _ _ .

b The hen had five little yellow c _ _ _ _ _ _ .

c Mrs Taylor and Mrs Patel stopped to have a c _ _ _ _ .

d Hannah had a nasty spot on her c _ _ _ .

e The c _ _ _ _ _ _ looked beautiful in the sunlight.

f Dad would not let me c _ _ _ the wood.

g The pirate kept his gold in a c _ _ _ _ _ .

h Black smoke came out of the tall c _ _ _ _ _ _ _ .

2 Work out the words below.

a _ _ ip

b fi _ _

c _ _ op

d di _ _

e _ _ ut

f wi _ _

g _ _ ed

h ra _ _

i _ _ ell

j _ _ oe

s or es

Rule 1

To make **one** word into **more than one** word add **s** or **es**.

For example: one egg   two eggs

one box   two boxes

1 Make **one** into **more than one** by adding **s** to the items below.

a one tree

b one shoe

c one book

d one apple

e one cake

f one chair

g one bean

h one car

2 Make **one** into **more than one** by adding **es**.

Use the words in the box to complete the sentences below.

church	class	dish	fox	glass	match

a It is dangerous to play with m _ _ _ _ _ _ .

b Claire drank two g _ _ _ _ _ _ of milk.

c There are three c _ _ _ _ _ _ _ in our town.

d Dad washed up and broke two d _ _ _ _ _ .

e There are ten c _ _ _ _ _ _ in our school.

f Two f _ _ _ _ ran across the field.

Pick and mix

help	left	sent	shade	shake
	shut	wash	went	

1 Use the words in the box to complete the sentences below.

   a Mum l _ _ _ her handbag on the bus.

   b Please _ _ _ t the door quietly.

   c Tasmin needed h _ _ _ with her homework.

   d It was so hot that we sat in the _ _ _ _ e.

   e Gran w _ _ _ for a walk in the garden.

   f Dad s _ _ _ Anita some flowers on her birthday.

   g I like thick milk sh _ _ _ .

   h Laura helped Dad _ _ sh the car.

2 Use the words in the box to sort out the jumbled words in **bold** in the sentences below.

able	always	clay	doing	little
	players	pretty	were	

   a Kylie **wysala** brushes her teeth at bedtime.

   b There are eleven **paeryls** in a football team.

   c Sue had a **ttllie** cut on her finger.

   d Jasmine made a model cat out of **lyca**.

   e Amy looked very **yttrep** in her new dress.

   f The poor dog was not **albe** to find its way home.

   g The twins **ewre** pleased with their birthday presents.

   h I have been **odgni** my homework.

st

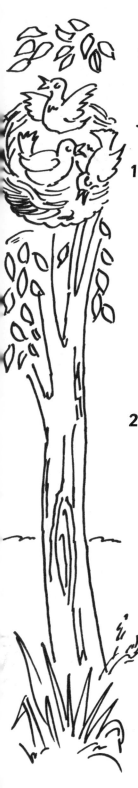

1 Give the fish a **st** head or a **st** tail.
Write the words in your book.

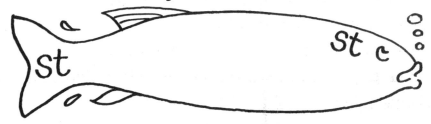

a _ _ amp   **b** _ _ ool   **c** _ _ ick   **d** _ _ em

e ne _ _   **f** _ _ op   **g** fi _ _   **h** po _ _

2 Use the words in the box to complete the sentences below.
Write them in your book.

> | | | |
> |---|---|---|
> | **fast** **nest** **stand** **started** | | |
> | **stripes** **stuck** **test** **toast** | | |

a A zebra has black and white s _ _ _ _ _ _.
b Sarah ran f _ _ _ and won the race.
c Joanne loves t _ _ _ _ and marmalade for breakfast.
d Kim s _ _ _ _ the picture into her album with glue.
e Mr Allport's class had an English t _ _ _.
f The blackbirds made a n _ _ _ in our tree.
g Wayne had to s _ _ _ _ on a chair to reach the shelf.
h The toddler fell over and s _ _ _ _ _ _ to cry.

ent

1 Use the words in the box to complete the
sentences below. Write them in your book.

bent	dent	lent	moment	present
	rent	sent	spent	tent

a The m _ _ _ _ _ Mum had gone the phone rang.

b I l _ _ _ the new boy my rubber.

c Jenny s _ _ _ _ all her money on videos.

d When I went camping I slept in a t _ _ _ .

e Mary s _ _ _ her cousin a birthday card.

f The new car had a d _ _ _ in the side.

g The video shop had a lot of films to r _ _ _ .

h The handle bars on my bike were b _ _ _ .

2 Copy the grid below into your book.

Use the clues in the box to find the missing words. Fill in the grid.

a	you might get one for your birthday	p						
b	you sleep in this outdoors	t						
c	I have _ _ _ _ _ all my money	s						
d	crooked	b						
e	a short time	m						

ing

1 Match the words below to the pictures. Write the words in your book.

ring   **king**   **swing**   **wing**   **sing**   **sling**

2 Complete the sentences below by adding **ing** to the words in the box.
Write the sentences in your book.

| cry   fish   fly   jump   play |
| sleep   talk |

a Tom and his friend have gone
  f _ _ _ _ _ _ today.

b The baby was c _ _ _ _ _ because
  she was hungry.

c The girls were j _ _ _ _ _ _ off the wall.

d My teacher was t _ _ _ _ _ _ to
  the class.

e Grandad likes s _ _ _ _ _ _ _ in his
  armchair.

f The bird was f _ _ _ _ _ higher and
  higher.

g I like p _ _ _ _ _ _ with my sister's
  computer.

th

1 Add **th** to complete the words below. Write them in your book.

a _ _ row   **b** _ _ rush   **c** _ _ ree

d _ _ orn   **e** _ _ umb

> **thorn   three   throw   thrush   thumb**

2 Copy the grid into your book. Use the words in the box and the clues to fill it in.

> **brother   father   mother   other**
> **than   that   then   they**

a now and _ _ _ _

b Mum

c Dad

d this and _ _ _ _

e This ball is better _ _ _ _ that ball.

f Tim is my big _ _ _ _ _ _ _ .

g I'd rather have the _ _ _ _ _ one.

h I know _ _ _ _ are late for school.

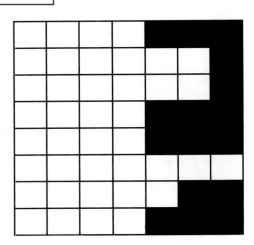

Silent w

1 Follow the lines and write the words in your book.

a wrinkle **b** wrist **c** wreck **d** wrong

2 Use the words on the worm to complete the sentences below.

Who whole wrap wriggle wrote

a Craig forgot to _ _ _ _ the present.
b Nina _ _ _ _ _ a letter to her friend.
c The _ _ _ _ _ cake was eaten at the party.
d A worm can _ _ _ _ _ _ _ into the soil.
e _ _ _ is your best friend?

United Kingdom

EDINBURGH

PENNINES

BELFAST

RIVER SEVERN

RIVER THAMES

CARDIFF

LONDON

Complete the sentences below and write them in your book.

1 The countries of the United Kingdom are E _ _ _ _ _ _ _ ,
W _ _ _ _ , S _ _ _ _ _ _ _ and N _ _ _ _ _ _ _ I _ _ _ _ _ _ .

2 The capital of England is L _ _ _ _ _ _ .   **odLnon**

3 The capital of Wales is C _ _ _ _ _ _ .   **ffCrdia**

4 The capital of Scotland is E _ _ _ _ _ _ _ _ .   **urbghniEd**

5 The capital of Northern Ireland is B _ _ _ _ _ _ .   **lefBsta**

6 The river that flows through London is
   called the T _ _ _ _ _ .   **maeThs**

7 The Pennine Chain is a
   range of m _ _ _ _ _ _ _ _ .   **aitounmns**

8 The Severn is the longest r _ _ _ _ in England.   **vrire**

9 Use the words in the box to complete
   the sentences below.

English   Welsh
Irish   Scottish

   a People who come from England
      are E _ _ _ _ _ _ _ .
   b If you come from Ireland you are
      I _ _ _ _ _ .
   c Andrew was born in Scotland, so
      he is S _ _ _ _ _ _ _ .
   d Megan comes from Wales, so she is
      W _ _ _ _ _ .

Days of the week

1 Put the days of the week below in order.
Write them in your book.

Wednesday
Friday
Monday
Thursday
Tuesday
Saturday
Sunday

Monday	Mark has geography at school.
Tuesday	Samantha goes to Brownies.
Wednesday	Mark does his homework.
Thursday	Rebecca and Sanjit go swimming.
Friday	shopping with Mum and Dad
Saturday	Elizabeth and Nayan go on a picnic.
Sunday	Andrew is making a racing car.

2 Use the grid to answer the questions below.

  a On W _ _ _ _ _ _ _ _ Mark does his homework.

  b Elizabeth and Nayan are having a picnic on S _ _ _ _ _ _ _ _ .

  c Samantha goes to Brownies on T _ _ _ _ _ _ .

  d F _ _ _ _ _ is shopping day.

  e Rebecca and Sanjit are going swimming on T _ _ _ _ _ _ _ _ .

  f On M _ _ _ _ _ Mark has geography at school.

  g On S _ _ _ _ _ Andrew is making a racing car.

Numbers

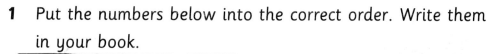

1 Put the numbers below into the correct order. Write them in your book.

nineteen	five	nine	one
three	eleven	thirteen	four
sixteen	fifteen	six	fourteen
two	eight	twelve	seven
ten	twenty	seventeen	eighteen

2 Write the sentences below into your book.
Use the numbers on the blackboard to help you.

a There are t _ _ _ _ _ months in a year.
b There are s _ _ _ _ days in one week.
c Half of twelve is s _ _ .
d There are e _ _ _ _ _ players in a football team.
e A half of four is t _ _ .

3 Use the words in the box to complete the sentences below. Write the sentences in your book.

half	**quarter**	**tenth**	**third**

a Fifteen minutes make a q _ _ _ _ _ _ _ of an hour.
b Six months is h _ _ _ a year.
c Ten is one t _ _ _ _ of a hundred.
d Andrew, Ela and Carmel had one t _ _ _ _ _ of the cake each.

Compass points

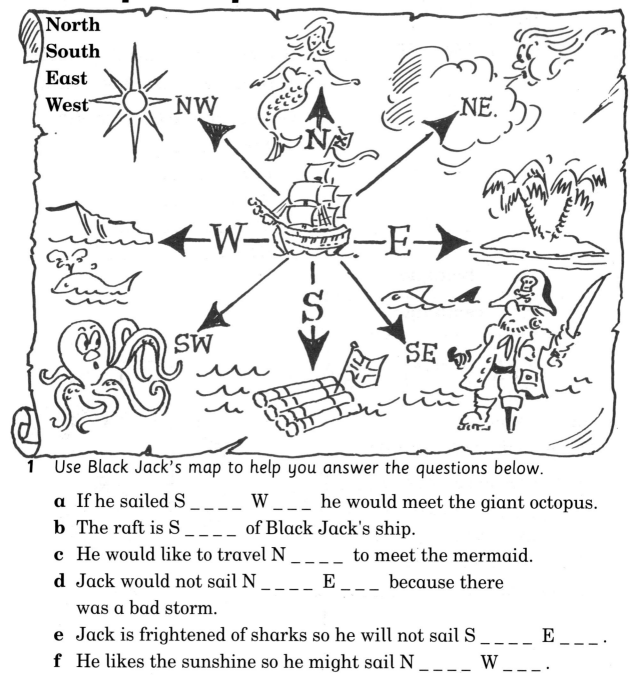

North
South
East
West

1 Use Black Jack's map to help you answer the questions below.

a If he sailed S _ _ _ _ W _ _ _ he would meet the giant octopus.

b The raft is S _ _ _ _ of Black Jack's ship.

c He would like to travel N _ _ _ _ to meet the mermaid.

d Jack would not sail N _ _ _ _ E _ _ _ because there
was a bad storm.

e Jack is frightened of sharks so he will not sail S _ _ _ _ E _ _ _ .

f He likes the sunshine so he might sail N _ _ _ _ W _ _ _ .

g If he sailed E _ _ _ he could play on the desert island.

h There are dangerous rocks if he sails to the W _ _ _ .

2 Write down what you would do to miss the rocks.

Shapes

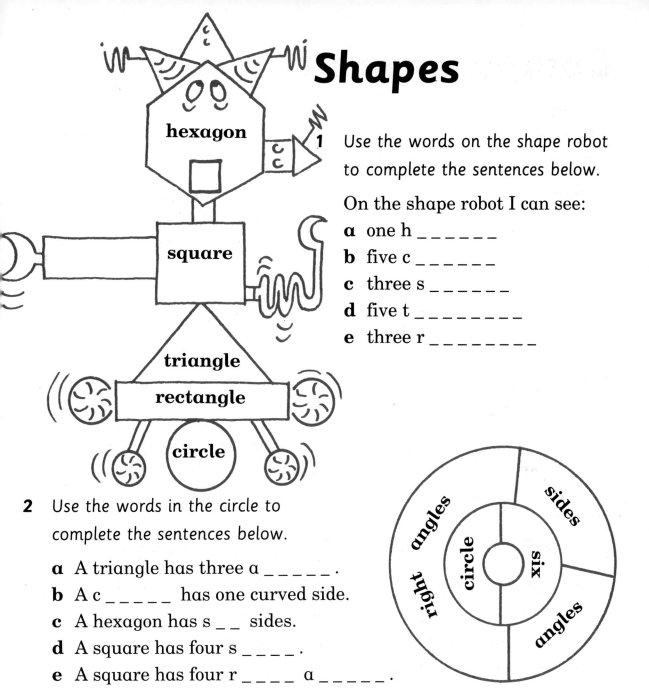

hexagon

square

triangle

rectangle

circle

1 Use the words on the shape robot to complete the sentences below.

On the shape robot I can see:
a one h _ _ _ _ _ _
b five c _ _ _ _ _ _
c three s _ _ _ _ _ _
d five t _ _ _ _ _ _ _
e three r _ _ _ _ _ _ _ _

2 Use the words in the circle to complete the sentences below.

a A triangle has three a _ _ _ _ _ .
b A c _ _ _ _ _ has one curved side.
c A hexagon has s _ _ sides.
d A square has four s _ _ _ _ .
e A square has four r _ _ _ _ a _ _ _ _ _ .

right angles   circle   six   sides   angles

Finishing post

START

1 Use the words in the box to complete the sentences below.

city	elbow	first	month	present
seven	south	stool	those	toes	triangle
Wales	washing	Wednesday	west	whole

a Rachel gave Jo a lovely birthday p _ _ _ _ _ _ .

b January is the first m _ _ _ _ of the year.

c Put t _ _ _ _ dirty old shoes in the bin.

d The little wooden s _ _ _ _ had three legs.

e Emily goes swimming every W _ _ _ _ _ _ _ _ .

f There are s _ _ _ _ days in a week.

g Emma ate the w _ _ _ _ Easter egg in one go.

h The opposite of north is s _ _ _ _ _ .

i Cardiff is the capital city of W _ _ _ _ _ .

j We have five t _ _ _ on each foot.

k John won f _ _ _ _ prize in the painting competition.

l A t _ _ _ _ _ _ _ _ has three sides and three angles.

m Nayan helped with the w _ _ _ _ _ _ - up after lunch.

n The Sun rises in the East and sets in the W _ _ _ .

o Liverpool is a c _ _ _ in the United Kingdom.

p Your e _ _ _ _ is the middle joint of your arm.

46

Word list

able	broom	cow	fast	half	June
acorn	brother	cry	father	happy	
all	bun	cube	Fawkes	hat	kick
always	bus	cup	feel	hay	kill
and	bush	cut	fell	head	king
angles	bushes	cute	fifteen	heel	knee
another	busy		fill	help	
ant	butter	Dad	fin	hexagon	lady
any	buy	day	fine	hibernate	lake
apples		deck	fingers	hid	leaves
art	cake	deep	fire	hide	led
ask	cakes	dent	fireworks	hill	left
Autumn	Cardiff	dig	first	his	leg
away	carry	dish	fish	hit	lent
	cars	dishes	fit	hold	letter
bag	case	dive	five	hole	lid
bank	cat	dock	flower	holiday	lie
bat	chairs	doctor	flute	hook	like
beans	chat	dog	fly	hoop	line
bed	cheese	doing	flying	hops	link
bee	chest	drive	fog	horses	lip
been	chicks	driver	foot	hose	little
Belfast	chimney	dry	forgot	hot	lock
bell	chin	dug	four	huge	London
bent	chips	duke	fourteen	hum	lorry
big	chop		fox	hut	
bill	Christmas	ear	foxes		made
bin	church	east	Friday	ice	make
bit	churches	Easter	friend	icy	man
black	circle	eating	frost	ill	mane
block	city	Edinburgh	fry	in	marry
blue	classes	egg	fun	ink	mask
bone	clay	eight	funny	into	matches
bonfire	clever	eighteen	fuse	Ireland	meet
book	clock	elbow		Irish	met
books	clown	eleven	glasses	ivy	mine
boot	coke	end	green		mole
born	comb	England	grey	jam	moment
bowl	cone	English	groom	jeep	Monday
box	cook		gun	job	moon
boxes	copy	face	Guy	joke	morning
boy	corn	family		jump	mother
bride	cot	farmer	had	jumping	month

mountain
mud
mug
Mum
my

name
near
neck
needs
nest
nice
nine
nineteen
north
nose
nut

old
one
open
other
oven
over

painting
pale
party
Passover
patches
path
peck
peel
pen
Pennines
pet
phone
pick
pie
pig
pill
pin
pine
pink
play
players

pool
pop
post
pot
present
presents
pretty
prize
purple
put

quarter

rabbits
rake
rank
rash
rat
rectangle
ray
red
reindeer
rent
report
rid
ride
right
ring
rip
ripe
river
road
role
roll
roof
room
rope
rose
rude
run

sad
sank
Santa
sat
Saturday

say
school
Scotland
Scottish
second
see
seed
seen
sell
sent
seven
seventeen
Severn
shade
shake
shed
sheep
shell
shine
ship
shoe
shoes
shook
shop
shorts
showers
shut
sick
sides
sing
singing
sink
sister
sit
six
sixteen
size
skate
ski
skill
sleep
sleigh
slide
sling
smiling
smoke

snake
soon
sore
sorry
sort
South
spent
spider
spill
spin
Spring
spy
square
stamp
stand
started
stem
stick
stool
stop
storm
stripes
struck
stuck
sty
Summer
Sun
Sunday
sunny
swing

take
talk
tank
tap
task
teacher
telephone
tell
ten
tent
tenth
test
Thames
than
thank

that
them
then
they
thick
think
third
thirteen
this
thorn
those
three
throw
thrush
thumb
thunder
Thursday
tick
tide
tie
time
tin
tip
toast
toes
tooth
top
torn
town
tray
tree
trees
triangle
try
tube
Tuesday
tug
tune
twelve
twenty
two

up
use
van
village

violet

wake
Wales
warm
wash
washing
way
weather
web
Wednesday
weed
week
well
Welsh
went
were
West
wet
white
who
whole
why
wig
wine
wing
wink
Winter
wish
with
woke
wood
worn
wrap
wreck
wriggle
wrinkle
wrinkles
wrist
writer
wrong
wrote

years
yellow